Shop ✓
    " ✓
      ✓
Woods ✓
wegarton ✓
left to enlist.
St Au...

Sho
Paint
Fen
co
wega

Cart

*For our editor Jackie Hamley,*
*who first brought Martin's art and my words together.*

**HR**

*For Emilie.*
*Thank you for showing me the magic of Heligan all those years ago.*

**MI**

*Produced in partnership with*
*The Lost Gardens of Heligan,*
*and with the generous support of*
*Trounce Guy, Ken Paynter and Penelope Willis.*

*first printed February 2017*

**STRAUSS HOUSE PRODUCTIONS**
www.strausshouseproductions.com

First published in Great Britain 2017
Text copyright © Hilary Robinson 2017
Illustrations copyright © Martin Impey 2017
Hilary Robinson and Martin Impey have asserted their rights
to be identified as the author and illustrator of this work under
The Copyright, Designs and Patents Act, 1988
British Library Cataloguing in Publication Data
A catalogue record for this book is available from the British Library
All rights reserved.
ISBN - 978-0-9571245-3-0
The author and illustrator would like to thank Heligan Archives
for permission to reproduce the photographs and painting on pages 66 & 67
Printed in the UK

# A SONG for WILL

## AND THE LOST GARDENERS OF HELIGAN

Written
by
**Hilary Robinson**

Illustrated
by
**Martin Impey**

**STRAUSS HOUSE**
PRODUCTIONS

*"I never remember Will as anything but content.*
*He was a gentle man.*
*After the war I went to see an uncle of ours*
*and I noticed he had a linnet in a cage on the kitchen table.*
*I asked him about it and he said,*
*'It was your Will that found it, crippled in a hedge.*
*He nursed it back to health.'"*

**Philip Guy**

The last four years have changed all our lives.

When war was declared in 1914, I was a young errand boy at Heligan and keen to sign up like the gardeners, but I wasn't old enough.

That day, all the outdoor staff wrote their names on the wall of the outdoor toilet, which we jokingly call the Thunderbox Room. I can't remember whose idea it was, it could have been the gardener William Guy's, as his name is near the top. Underneath their list they recorded the date: August 1914.

"One day, Alfie," said Fred Paynter, the stonemason, as he etched his name on the lime plaster, "people might look at our names and remember what courageous young men we were!"

What we didn't know was that this would be the last time we would all be together.

And now it's 1918, war is over and we have a new beginning.

Looking at the names on the Thunderbox wall, thinking about who is coming back and who isn't, I know that life at Heligan will never quite be the same again.

This is our story.

March 1915
Salisbury Plain

Dear Alfie,

Well, we finally left St Austell with a real sense of adventure.
There wasn't as much cheering and hat throwing as on the day
The Naval Reserve left last August. It was good of so many to
turn out though. I looked for you, Alfie, but couldn't see you.

Few of us have ever travelled away from home before and
now we have arrived on Salisbury Plain to begin training.

I know they said the war would be over by last Christmas, so I
can understand how anxious you all must be at Heligan. We are
keeping our spirits up though and perhaps we will be home for
the herring season next winter. If not, and with so many
fishermen in the forces now, you may have to go and fish for
them yourself!

The good news is that William Guy and I are still together at
the moment. Will asked me to remind you to take care of
Willow. He says, "She is a horse in a million", and he can't wait
to see her when he returns.

We look forward to hearing your news of Heligan and the
gardens, Alfie. Make sure Mr Griffin doesn't let anyone
whitewash over the Thunderbox wall where we wrote our
names. We hope they will stay there forever.

Yours,
Fred

May 1915
Heligan Gardens

Dear Fred,

We were all excited to hear your news. Mr Griffin read
your letter to all the outdoor staff and then Daisy read
it to the staff in the Mansion. It made me proud to
think a real soldier had written to me. I tried to write
back but found it difficult so my old school teacher,
Mr Hunkin, is helping me now.

I tried to catch up when you took the bus up the valley
but my bike had a puncture. I ran up to the cliff top
though and saw you disappear into the distance.

I do wish I had been old enough to join up. Mother
says I mustn't get my hopes up for the future as I am
pigeon-chested and that could mean I fail the medical.
The war could be over by then though. Mr Griffin has
put a map up on the wall in his office so that we can
see where you all are when you write to us from Europe.

Everyone has extra jobs to do at Heligan now, with so
many away at war. So, as well as being the errand boy,
I help in the Kitchen Garden too. I got a bonus this
week for catching four rats! I think of them as the
enemy and lie in wait to capture them.

The Squire and his mother are here whenever they can be. The Squire is often in London enlisting men for The Duke of Cornwall's Light Infantry. Mrs Tremayne wants to support the local people as much as possible. She says, "This is a terribly worrying time for many families."

Would you tell Will that no one stays up all night in the bothy above the Thunderbox Room anymore, to watch out for the manure in the Pineapple Pit self-combusting! Mr Griffin says that our time now can be better served and the last thing we want is explosions at Heligan as there's enough of that going on in Europe. He says, "Pineapples are a luxury to grow and a time of war is not a time for luxury."

Yours,

Alfie

June 1915
Heligan Gardens

Dear Fred,

I bumped into Joe Pengelly when I was out doing errands yesterday. Joe and I were at school together and he looked really smart in his new uniform. He says he wishes he could have volunteered too but he is enjoying his new job as a Telegram Messenger Boy. We made a pledge that we will try and enlist together as soon as we are old enough. He is worried he may fail a medical too because he has asthma. Tell Will that Joe is learning to play the accordion. I remember Will was saving all his rat-catching money to buy a harmonium and Joe says he hopes to be good enough to play with Will when the war is over.

Tell Will also that Daisy works with us in the garden now as well as helping Ida cook in the kitchen.

Do you remember the injured linnet that Will found by the little Handkerchief Tree in the Sun-Dial Garden? Daisy says she sings every morning. We tried to get her to fly away but she wouldn't go. The Handkerchief Tree still hasn't flowered. Mr Griffin says it may take a few years yet.

We have called the linnet Hope, as we hope that you will all return, safe and well. She likes to fly around the Peach House where Will sometimes used to work and she seems quite happy.

Yours,

Alfie

July 1915
Salonika

Dear Alfie,

Thank you for your letters. It is good to hear about the gardens and stories from home. We do miss everyone.

I have been posted to The Balkans and things are not as peaceful here. I had been working as part of The Royal Army Medical Corps at the Valetta Hospital in Malta. Mr Griffin will be able to show you on the map. The days were long and hot and the palms reminded me of Heligan so, in some ways, it felt like home. There are 27 hospitals in Malta, all full of injured soldiers. Many of them are ANZACs, soldiers from Australia and New Zealand. They've travelled thousands of miles to support us and so many died when they attacked Gallipoli.

I sometimes hear from Will who is now in France and being trained to fight on the front line. Through the Army we are able to get messages to each other. The last time I heard from him he said he was sitting in a tent listening to the rain as there was no drill. He said he keeps thinking about the fine food we grew at Heligan. All he has now is ten ounces of meat and eight ounces of vegetables a day, and they only have two vats to cook everything in, so their tea often tastes of onions!

Will said weeds and nettles are being used in soup and stews there. It makes me laugh to think how he cleared the gardens of weeds and now he is having them for supper!

Will also said he doesn't hear many different birds singing on the battlefield now, just the song of the skylarks. He said the corn poppies that thrive in the battlefields remind him of home.

Yours,

Fred

October 1915
Heligan Gardens

Dear Fred,

It was good to hear from you. Daisy and Ida are
using weeds in cooking now too, as food is in short
supply. They made nettle soup yesterday and we all
thought it was tasty. Daisy talks a lot about Will.
I think she misses him. Ida keeps teasing her about
him and she goes all red and says, "Stop it, Ida,
you're making me blush."

The Squire likes to sit in the Italian Garden with Pip
and Pepper. All but one of his five nephews have
gone to war now. Ralph is still too young and must
stay at Eton, but apparently he can't wait to follow
his brothers and will be going to Sandhurst to train
next year. Hugh is serving on the submarines. Ida says
she doesn't think the officers will be any safer than
our staff though, as she says, "War knows no rank."
Please keep safe Fred. We worry that you are now in
more dangerous territory and we are all praying for
your safe return.

Yours,

Alfie

October 1915
Heligan Gardens

Dear Fred,

Joe popped by yesterday to collect some flowers from
Mrs Tremayne for a family in Mevagissey whose son was
killed in battle. He says he really dreads delivering
telegrams to families with the terrible news that a
member of their family has died, and he has an
arrangement with Mrs Tremayne to take flowers from
Heligan to them all.

Mrs Tremayne cuts the flowers herself when she is here.
She says that, "Every soldier lost is a mother's son."
Ida says, "Mrs Tremayne is a font of wisdom."
I delivered bramblings to the vicar in St Ewe for the
Harvest Festival. He asked me to tell you that you are
both in his prayers.

I saw Diggory Abbott while I was there too. He said he
is enjoying his new gardening job but misses Heligan.
I told him he is still there as we have a
scarecrow in the Kitchen Garden
named after him! I'm not sure
how he felt about that! I will keep
you posted on news from Heligan
and in the meantime, stay safe.

Yours,
Alfie

WELCOME
to
ALL SAINTS CHURCH
ST EWE
THIS SUNDAY
HARVEST
FESTIVAL

November 1915
Salonika

Dear Alfie,

We shall be moving shortly to the front line so I may not get as much time to write. I am now serving with The Royal Engineers, which is a bit more in keeping with my old job as a stonemason at Heligan.

As we head towards winter, please keep your letters coming. Will told me to remind you to drag seaweed from Portmellon - it's a good fertiliser and won't cost a penny, and don't forget to double dig either! Will said the gardeners called it trenching and now we are digging our own trenches on the battlefield. I expect Mr Griffin is making sure you are all doing this, but thinking of the gardens helps us to cope with life here.

We would far rather be at Heligan digging up vegetables for food than digging to hide for safety. It is getting tough, Alfie, but Will is to be home on leave in a few months. He is looking forward to seeing his family and seeing Hope again - and, of course, seeing Daisy.

Tell Daisy we have Tickler's jam here, sent all the way from Grimsby. It's not as good as the blackberry jam she makes at Heligan though.

Yours,

Fred

November 1915
Heligan Gardens

Dear Fred,

The trenching has begun here! I never knew that was also the word for double digging, so now I pretend I am a soldier like you.

It was really blowy at Portmellon when Daisy and I went down to drag seaweed. Sea spray gushed over Willow but she seemed to like it.

Joe said that he was in St Austell last August when 130 horses went off to war. 130! They were checking out the farm horses gathered in the yard at the White Hart when the clay wagons arrived and the drivers offered their horses too! They were all classed as fit and each horse was branded. There was much cheering and many tears as they were led away to war. Then the drivers had to work out how to get back home without their horses!

The Squire said we might need to let Willow go one day and maybe even Pip and Pepper, as dogs are also proving useful for the war effort. I don't like to think about animals going away. If Willow does have to go, I hope she is able to serve with Will.

Yours,

Alfie

November 1915
Heligan Gardens

Dear Fred,

Daisy saw Will's mother last Sunday in chapel. She told Daisy she is glad she still has all her other children at home to keep her mind off the worry of Will. Daisy gave her some honey and beeswax. Ida said that women are allowed to take the collection in church now that so many men are away. Mr Griffin shook his head and said, "Whatever next!"

Those Bee Boles you mended in the wall near the Kitchen Garden, Fred, have been really helpful. Ida says that sugar is going up in price quickly. She and Daisy are now cooking with honey instead of sugar. Everything is in short supply so everyone is being asked to grow more of their own food, particularly cabbages and potatoes. Ida keeps telling us that if we don't behave she'll be serving up cabbage crumble!

The Squire and Mr Griffin have organised for some of us to help local people start more allotments. We don't have much time though as there's only half the staff left now and so many extra jobs to do.

Yours,

Alfie

December 1915
Heligan Gardens

Dear Fred,

Daisy said that Hope sings every day in the Sun-Dial Garden. She said, "If it helps to bring peace then that would be a good thing." I said I thought it would take more than that. She then got all upset with me and Ida made me go and say sorry, although I didn't really know what I'd done wrong. Ida said, "We all have our little ways of making ourselves feel better, Alfie, and if Hope helps Daisy then so be it."

We have gathered in the holly for the mansion and Mrs Tremayne said we must keep things simple. She said money and supplies are short and we must all "make do". I saved some holly to put up in the Thunderbox Room, just above your names.

The snow fell last night. I hope it is not as cold for you there as it is here. The ground is hard so we are cleaning pots and repairing tools in the Potting Shed.

If I don't hear from you before, we all wish you a Happy Christmas and hope that it is peaceful. Keep dreaming of Heligan, Fred. It will be here, just as you left it, when you come home.

Yours, Alfie

January 1916
Salonika

Dear Alfie,

Happy New Year!
There was no Christmas Truce for us like last year but we all entered
into the spirit of the season and folk back home have been very kind.
We received chocolates, sweets and Christmas puddings, which we all
shared between us.

Can you believe this? A soldier in our battalion had a lucky escape.
A bullet that would have taken his life became lodged in a tin of toffee
in his breast pocket. Talk about a close call!

It's not all doom and gloom Alfie, so please don't worry. Yes it is bitterly
cold and wet in the trenches, particularly now, and there are rats the
size of cats. We have made some great friends though and we all help
to keep each other's spirits up by telling jokes and singing.

The thoughts of returning to Heligan keep me going. Even smoking out the
honeybees from the Bee Boles and leaping out of the way of them
would be a pleasure now – and I never thought I'd hear myself say that!
Mosquitoes and the threat of malaria here make a bee sting seem like a
scratch. All that certainly seems worth it for a slice of Ida's honey cake.

Yours,

Fred

May 1916
Heligan Gardens

Dear Fred,

You will never guess what happened!
I was busy picking strawberries when
who should stride up the path, looking
smart in his uniform, but Will! Hope flew
round his cap and landed in the palm
of his hand, as if he'd never left.

I noticed that Will's hand was shaking – he must have
been excited to be back. I wouldn't have believed that a
bird could remember the man who saved her but it looks
like she did!

Daisy ran out of the kitchen to greet him, forgetting she
had flour on her hands! Will smiled and said he'd like to
try some of her nettle soup. Ida went into a panic and let
the soup boil over and there was all kinds of chaos in
the kitchen.

Will said it was tough for you all and he had seen things
he never wanted to see again. I asked him lots of
questions, but I could tell he didn't want to talk about
it. He did say he always felt relieved when he knew you
were safe. He wished you could have served together.
Will enjoyed walking around the grounds and Willow
jumped for joy when she saw him! She galloped right
across the field to greet him!

Joe turned up. They sat in the Sun-Dial Garden and he taught Will to play 'Keep the Home Fires Burning' on his accordion while Hope hopped about on the grass. Will said he got a "King's Shilling" for joining up and that he nearly has enough to buy his harmonium now. He hopes that he and Joe will play duets one day. Ida could hear them and she kept getting upset as she kneaded the dough, saying things like, "What that boy's poor mother must be going through." Ida's nephew, Albert, is on the front line and she seems to talk about little else.

When Will left, he whistled as he walked away. Then he turned round and waved as he disappeared over the brow of the hill. Keep safe, Fred! Ida says she can't cope with much more and neither can we.

Yours,

Alfie

June 1916
Heligan Gardens

Dear Fred,

The weather here is lovely. Daisy and I have started a medicinal herb garden because the Squire has decided that the Mansion should become a convalescence hospital for injured officers. We are finding out how different plants can help injuries and cure diseases. The Squire said that Heligan will be a fitting place to recover. Did you know the letters of "Heligan" also spell "Healing"?

Fred! You will never believe what we saw! All the staff ran out of the Mansion and the gardeners dropped their tools and we all raced over to West Lawn. We had never seen anything like it – a huge, hovering balloon over Mevagissey! I was scared at first but Mr Griffin said I was not to worry as it was just a British airship patrolling the coastline and keeping a check on things.

I did wonder if the Squire's nephew, John, who is a pilot, might be in it and waving to us and if he might land in the cornfields. Mr Griffin said it was unlikely as John is currently swooping around Europe in his small Avro biplane "doing heroic things". It seems the war is creeping ever closer to us here now. Keep safe, Fred.
Yours,

Alfie

August 1916
Salonika

Dear Alfie,

I'm sure you'll have heard that there was a "Big Push" on The Somme in France at the start of July. It didn't quite go to plan and we have heard that our losses have been considerable. There are no words, Alfie, no words. I have yet to hear from Will, so we pray he is safe.

I suppose we should be relieved that Willow is still safe in her stable at Heligan. It's a fitting place for her to be, given that Heligan is Cornish for willow tree. Did you know that, Alfie?

It was good to hear your news about the medicinal herb garden. Quite a few herbs are being used to treat the injured here. Garlic and sage are antiseptics and they are cleaning the hospital walls with lavender water. Even marigolds are being used to help to treat burns.

We have all been issued with gas masks, which are uncomfortable and difficult to wear. But, having seen the damage that gas attacks can do, I'm not complaining. We have been warned the gas has a sweet smell, a little like pear drops. If there is any sign of it we should be alert for the call of "GAS" and a bell ringing, or a rattle, and then put on our masks immediately. It is the most dangerous of weapons. But worry not! Everything is being done to keep us as safe as possible. Maybe if we bring our masks back with us, they might help to protect us when we're cutting up onions – and we might even scare the bees!

Yours,

Fred

October 1916
Heligan Gardens

Dear Fred,

Thank you for your letter. We are all very worried about you both and especially Will at the moment. His family are anxious, too. No one seems to know how he is and whether he survived The Somme. Prayers were said for him in the chapel at Gorran Highlanes and Ida keeps saying, "No news is good news", but Mr Griffin says we should prepare for the worst.

Daisy and I like to walk in the Sun-Dial Garden on what we call our "worry days". We find it peaceful there, for even though the seasons change, the gardens always remind us of everyone who has left.

After seeing my first airship, I have now seen the new tanks! Mr Griffin showed us all a picture of them in the newspaper and we've stuck it up in the Potting Shed. They must seem very scary to the enemy. Mr Griffin hopes that tanks might be just what is needed to turn the tide of war in our favour.

Please take care, Fred. I am not sure we can cope with more devastating news here.

Yours,

Alfie

February 1917
Heligan Gardens

Dear Fred,

All is well! A few days ago
Will's mother turned up to tell
us his Field Service Post Card had been delayed in the
post but he was safe. I can't tell you how relieved we
all were Fred. Then Will surprised us at the kitchen
door! He'd been allowed home on leave. He said he'd
been able to let you know that he was ok.

More good news is that he's finally saved up enough
money to buy a harmonium, and he and Daisy took the
train to Truro to order it. It was the highlight of his
leave! But Daisy is worried about him. His youngest
brother Philip told her that Will's hand was shaking so
much in chapel that he couldn't read the words from
the hymnbook they shared.

It was a bit emotional when Will left. As a parting gift
he gave Daisy a little Yellow Clouded Butterfly. He said
it couldn't fly when he found it but it was fine now. We
let it free in the field beside the emu run. He whistled
again as he left, and Daisy and I stood and listened
until we could hear him no more.

This time he didn't turn and wave at
the brow of the hill like he did before.

Yours, *Alfie*

April 1917
Heligan Gardens

Dear Fred,

I thought you would like to know that things are cheering up here. After all the worrying news, Heligan seems a bit more like its old self, even though there are only five gardeners left now.

The Squire held a garden party for our injured servicemen on Flora's Green last week. It wasn't like the bazaars they used to have because the food supply is so short and money too. But he said it was a good opportunity to bring people together at Easter.

Daisy made some bunting from old dusters and cloths. She organised an Easter egg hunt, the town band played and the Morris dancers got Ida to join in! She looked very much the part waving her handkerchiefs, hitching up her long skirt and skipping around! Even the Squire's pet monkey enjoyed it.

There was a cricket match between St Ewe and Gorran, which included teams of both men and women. The match was declared a draw. Mr Griffin said, "Women playing cricket, whatever next! They'll give women the vote before we know it."

We ran a scarecrow competition and lots of children took part. Diggory Abbott, "The Scarecrow of Honour", was the judge and there was an Easter bonnet competition, which Daisy won. She made her own from golden straw and decorated it with wild flowers.

Daisy and Ida have been preserving food all year, including eggs, and they served up Cornish pasties, honey cake and scones with strawberry jam and cream from the Squire's Jersey cows. Ida says she might write a cookbook one day and Daisy is starting a scrapbook with pressed herbs.

Later we all sat round a bonfire and Joe played 'Keep the Home Fires Burning' on his accordion. He's getting good at that!

The most incredible thing happened, Fred. One blind serviceman was walking around the garden with the Squire and Pepper, when the Squire was called away. We noticed that Pepper took over and was guiding the officer around the grounds, making sure he didn't bump into anything! The Squire said that it was quite incredible, that a dog should sense that a man can't see.

The injured officers are all from The Royal Flying Corps and enjoy being here. Despite their wounds and the suffering, they all say it is lovely to breathe the fresh Cornish air and just sit, in peace, in our beautiful gardens.

We all send our love and hope you are keeping safe, Fred.
Yours,

Alfie

PS It looks like Mrs Tremayne's Handkerchief Tree in the Sun-Dial Garden might bloom for the first time this year.

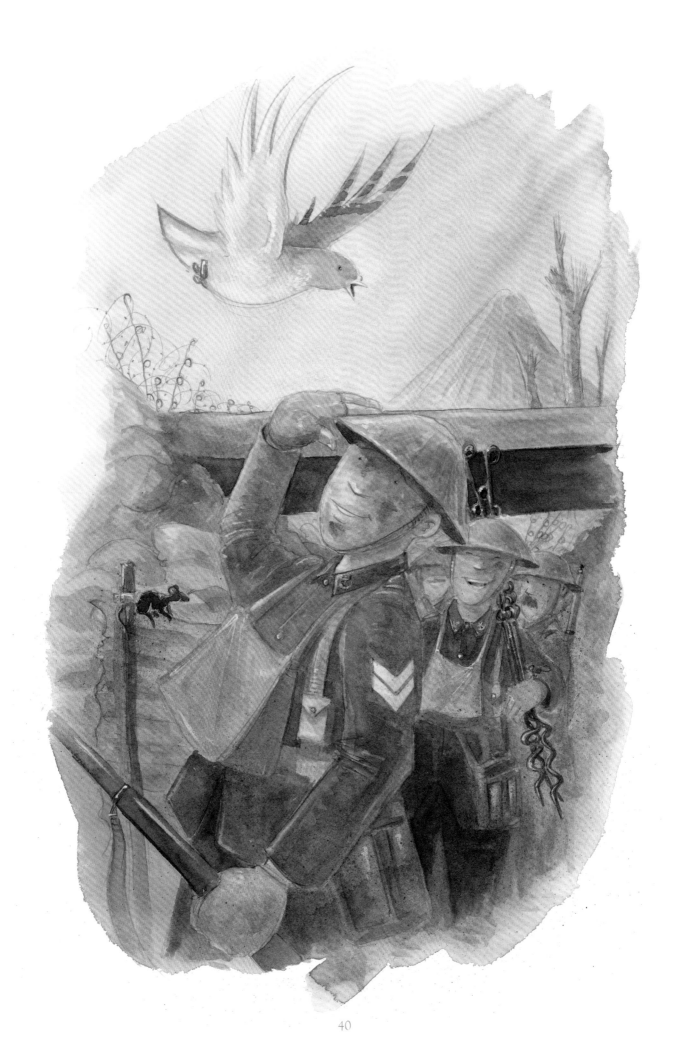

August 1917
Salonika

Dear Alfie,

How cheered I was to read about the gathering on Flora's Green! It is great to know that even when all seems bleak you are able to muster up enough enthusiasm to celebrate the good things in life.

It doesn't surprise me about Pepper. We have found that dogs seem to have a sixth sense and have done much to look after us all. They are being used now to take first aid kits across the battlefields so that injured soldiers can tend their own wounds until the stretcher-bearers arrive. There have been astonishing acts of bravery by pigeons too, dodging the bullets and bombs to bring messages back to base.

There is brighter news Alfie, so please tell everyone. Will has been made a Corporal! That is a fine achievement for him but he is in dangerous territory so we hope and pray he will stay safe. I have been in a few close scrapes myself but please be reassured that I am safe and well.

Yours,

Fred

March 1918
Heligan Gardens

Dear Fred,

I just had to write to you as there is much concern
here about serious casualties again at the front and
neither Daisy nor Mrs Guy have heard from Will.
Ida doesn't know if it's a good thing or not to get
the newspaper each day as she says it only causes us
to worry needlessly. Her nephew, Albert, was "missing
presumed dead" and then turned up safe and well,
but confused.

Willow has seemed restless lately. We are not sure
if she is unwell or if something else is bothering her.
She seems to fret constantly in her stable and needs
a lot of coaxing to come out.

Yours,

Alfie

April 1918
Heligan Gardens

Dear Fred,

We have had such bad news. Our worst fears have been realised and the Squire says you will already know by now.

Daisy was delivering Heligan eggs in Gorran Haven and saw Joe's bicycle outside Will's house. She came running back all upset so I jumped on my bike to see if I could find Joe.

The door to Will's house was open and I could see his mother had a telegram in her hand. She was crying. I couldn't see Joe anywhere. It turns out that he'd disappeared up the street to deliver three more telegrams with bad news.

Then the Squire called us all together. He said, "I had hoped this day would never come, but I am sorry to say our dearest Will has been killed in action."

I cannot find the words to explain how we all felt. There was, for what seemed like ages, silence, and I honestly thought the Squire might cry. He blinked and swallowed hard.

Gorran Parish alone has now lost 15 men in this war. Whole villages are losing their young men, Fred; sons, brothers, fathers, uncles. Even the Squire, who has always been so positive, said, "Nothing can match the misery and tragedy of this wicked war."

Daisy cut some flowers to take to Will's mother – the first pickings of Sweet William from the garden. She stayed with her for a while.

Ida keeps sobbing into her pinny and saying, "I always had a soft spot for Will, such a gentle man, such a kind and warm gentleman. He always left a piece of his morning cake for the birds and would often go without if there wasn't enough."

Daisy is so upset. She sits at the kitchen table weeping all the time. Ida just gives her easy jobs like hanging out the dusters. Daisy said she can't bring herself to get excited about making cakes and fancy things like that and she's not sure she can ever listen to a harmonium again. She said that even Hope has not sung since we heard the news about Will.

There was a special service in the chapel at Gorran Highlanes for Will. We all wore black armbands and we took Willow and tied black ribbons in her mane. She didn't need persuading to come out of her stable this time and she waited patiently by the chapel gates. I think she sensed what the service was for.

Please take care and come home safely.
Yours,
Alfie

August 1918
France

Dear Alfie,

Thank you for your letter and sorry for the delay in writing but
I have been on the move once again and am now back in France.

I am afraid that I did know about Will and again, words fail me.
I wonder sometimes whether this is all worth it. To see how war
has torn this country apart too is tragic, Alfie. Fine architecture
reduced to ruins, fields of golden corn now muddy pits. But no
matter how bad things get, we take heart in the fact that nature
always asserts itself — war cannot cripple it — the sun still
shines, wild flowers bloom and the skylarks keep singing.

I am now with The 166th Battalion Tank Regiment. It is hard to get excited about new machinery when those we know and love have perished, but these iron monsters are something else, Alfie. They are huge, heavy vehicles, a bit like a steam tractor, and baking hot, noisy and cramped. The hope is that the tanks will keep us safe.

It is difficult to feel positive now when I think of our dear friend, Will. When I heard the news, all I could think of was how unsuited to war he really was but what a good job he had made of it. No other man from Heligan has reached such a high rank.

Will joined up, like the rest of us, because he felt it was just, and because it was right, but he always was a sensitive soul who loved gardening, music and caring for wildlife. That's where his heart was, nurturing and saving life, not taking it. The world has lost one that would protect the weakest.

Here, in this folded sheet of paper, are some poppy seed cases. I had them sent specially from the battlefield where Will was lost. When they are dry, Alfie, please scatter them somewhere special at Heligan. I know poppies are considered the farmer's weed but we have learned even weeds have value, especially in war, and when they flower they will remind us of a gentle man of faith and peace.

Nature has a way of easing the pain. Will's spirit will always be at Heligan and he will never be forgotten.

Yours,

*Fred*

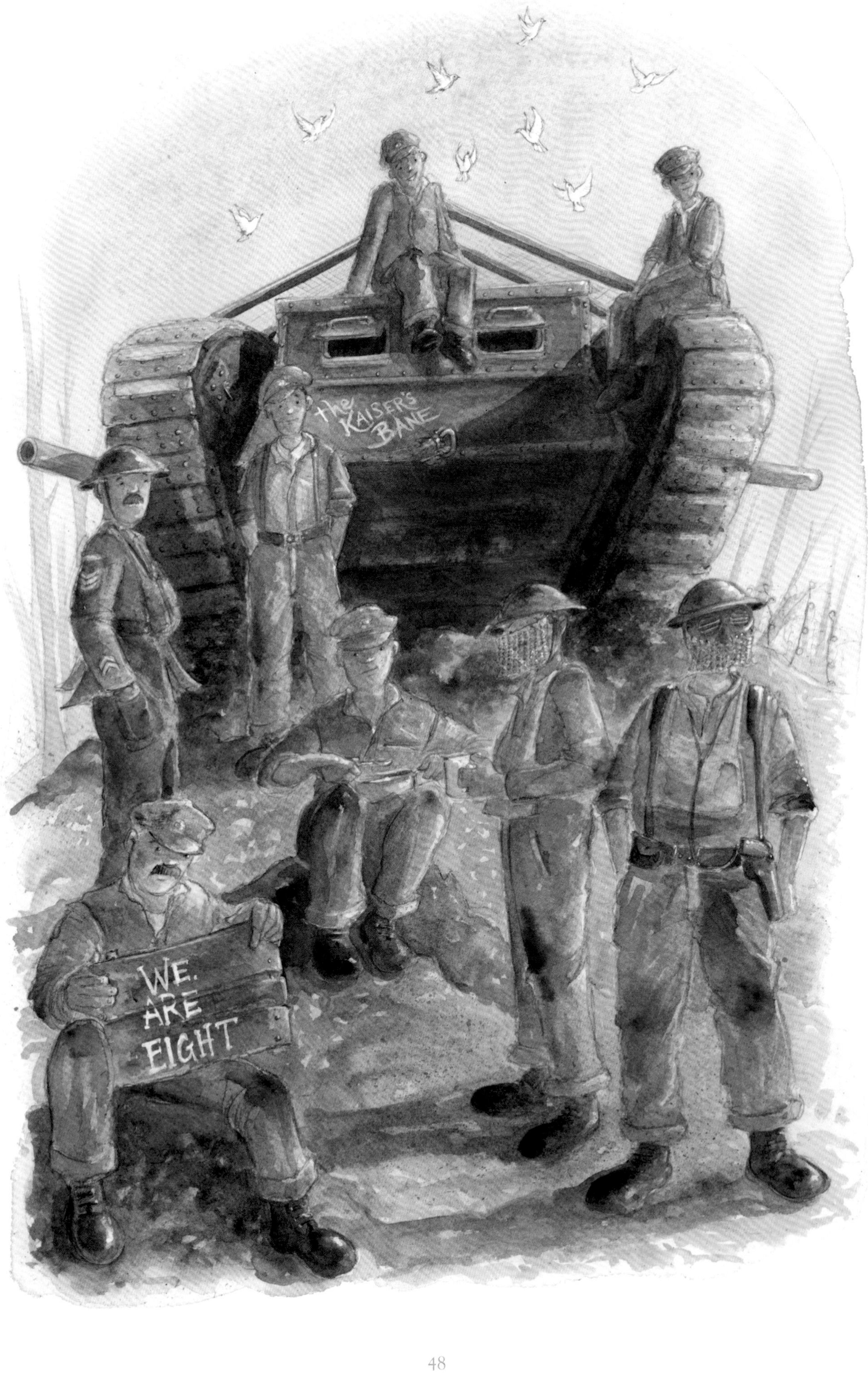
the Kaiser's Bane
WE ARE EIGHT

September 1918
France

Dear Alfie,

I am writing in haste just to let you know in case you read about it in the paper, but a flu virus has spread through the ranks here and laid many of us low. I got pneumonia and ended up in hospital. The day after I was taken in, my tank was blown up and all my friends were killed, including the poor soldier who replaced me. These tanks that were supposed to protect us and keep us safe are still vulnerable to attack. It could so easily have been me Alfie, I feel so guilty. Guilty that I have survived while others have perished. I hear a lot of soldiers say the same.

We have heard word that this dreadful war may be coming to an end. We hope and pray that this is the case and that we can come home to Blighty, to our families and for me, to Heligan too.

Yours,

Fred

11 November 1918
Heligan Gardens


Dear Fred,


Today the Squire called us all together in the Mansion
drawing room. He said he finally had some good news to
share with us but we should be mindful of all those who had
suffered over the last four years. He said we would no doubt
read about it in the paper but he was relieved and pleased to
be able to say that the war was finally over. Peace had been
officially declared. Ida almost fainted and Daisy had
to help her sit down in Mrs Tremayne's best chair, she was
so overcome.


You would expect us to rejoice Fred, but in fact the
atmosphere was one of relief more than anything. Daisy cried
because she said Will so nearly survived the war and it was
such a shame he never got to play his harmonium. The Squire
asked us to think of all the families who were grieving.
He said it was a time of joy but also a time to be thankful
and we should be respectful as we go about our business,
both at Heligan and beyond.

I thought you would be coming home straight away, but the Squire said it would take many weeks, maybe months, to get everyone home. Those who were the last to sign up, and who are fit for work, will be the first to be repatriated as there is much to be done here now to get the country back on its feet. I hope it doesn't take too long – we can't wait to see you!

Daisy and I walked up to the Sun-Dial Garden to take a look at the Handkerchief Tree. All that is left on the branches at the moment are a few round dark seed cases that remind us of bullets.

Fred, I can't tell you how happy we are that you are coming back to Heligan! We have sown some of the poppy seeds by Willow's stable and the rest by the Handkerchief Tree, but still Hope has not sung.

Yours,

Alfie

## Alfie's Diary

It was Daisy who spotted him. We were all having our morning break and she was looking out of the window. She saw someone walking down the back lane.

It was Fred! "Fred!" she said, "Fred's back!" We all ran out to meet him.

We couldn't believe it. There had been rumours that he was back but Mr Griffin told us to let him have some private time with his family over at St Ewe first. Yet it seemed wrong, in some ways, to celebrate a homecoming when so many had lost their lives.

Fred hugged us all and the Squire came out and walked with him in the grounds. They went over to see Willow, grazing in the field. She is more settled these days.

Fred didn't seem the same really. He was gaunt and unsteady, but like Ida said, "Who would be the same, after all that he had seen?" It must have been hard for him to come back to Heligan knowing that so many of the others wouldn't be here ever again, especially his best friend, Will.

I went up to the Thunderbox Room and stared at the wobbly signatures on the bumpy lime plaster walls with the unforgettable date: August 1914. I read each name out loud and as I did so, I felt Fred's hand on my shoulder. He joined in with me, calling the names as well. This place now feels like a precious memorial.

We walked down to the kitchen together and chatted while Ida served us hot tea and Fred's favourite honey cake. He said how much he liked receiving my letters and how he has saved every single one. I told him I had saved his too and that I would keep them safe forever.

Fred asked how the poppy seeds were doing and he asked about Hope. Daisy said Hope hadn't sung since we heard the news about Will, and that she hadn't seen her in quite a few days either, which was most unusual.

Fred had tears in his eyes. I had never seen him like that before.

Fred wanted to see where the poppies had been sown. So we set off to Willow's stable. Then we walked over to meet everyone in the Sun-Dial Garden. Joe turned up with his accordion. He said he had "practised and practised" to make sure he was note perfect for Will.

Looking down, we could hardly believe that the poppy seeds from Will's battlefield had burst into life and one bud was just opening, as if to remind us that Will's spirit lives on. Then we were left speechless, as we looked up and noticed the first new white bracts on the little Handkerchief Tree, each gently spreading out like the wings of a dove.

The Squire looked thoughtful and then said, "Now the doves of peace have landed here, it might be fitting to rename the tree. It is time to put away our handkerchiefs. From this day forward, we will call it by its other name, the 'Dove Tree'. The suffering is finally over and we can look forward, with hope, to a more peaceful future."

Remembering all our friends and relatives who sacrificed their lives so that we might live in peace,
Joe played again, note perfect,
'Keep the Home Fires Burning'. Then, just
as he finished, the most amazing thing
happened.

Hope flew into the Dove Tree, and
started to sing her heart out!
It was the most sweet and
beautiful song.

We smiled through our tears for
it was clear to all of us that this
time, Hope, the little linnet saved
by a kind and gentle gardener, was
singing not just her own birdsong,
but... a Song for Will.

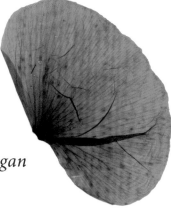

# The Lost

*In memory of the nine outdoor staff of Heligan
who gave their lives in World War 1*

*Poppy petals collected from West Lawn in July 2016,
while Heligan was Remembering the Somme.*

**Charles Ball - *Road Man***

*Enlisted - unknown - joined 10th Battalion The Worcestershire Regiment*
*Died of wounds 3rd April 1918 at Bapaume - 41 years old*
*He rests in Etaples Military Cemetery.*

**John George Barron - *Gardener***

*Enlisted - November 1914 - joined 1st Battalion The Duke of Cornwall's Light Infantry*
*Killed in Action 23rd July 1916 at Delville Wood - 21 years old*
*His name is on the Thiepval Memorial to the Missing.*

**Percy Carhart - *Labourer***

*Enlisted - June 1916 - joined 1st Battalion The Duke of Cornwall's Light Infantry*
*Killed in Action 30th October 1917 Polderhoek area, Passchendaele - 19 years old*
*His name is on the Tyne Cot Memorial to the Missing.*

**Charles Dyer - *Gardener***

*Enlisted - August 1914 - already with The Royal Naval Reserve at the outbreak of war*
*Wounded aboard His Majesty's Trawler "Rosa". Died 24th May 1918 nr Chatham - 35 years old*
*He rests in St Peter's Cemetery, Mevagissey.*

**William Robins Guy - *Gardener***
*Enlisted - August 1914 - joined The Duke of Cornwall's Light Infantry*
*Killed in Action 13th April 1918 at Calonne - 23 years old*
*His name is on the Loos Memorial to the Missing.*

**William Samuel Hunkin - *Labourer***
*Called up - August 1914 - joined the Royal Naval Reserve at the outbreak of war*
*Served and died aboard HMS "Challenger" 12th October 1914 - 35 years old*
*He rests in Douala Cemetery, Cameroon.*

**William George Perry - *Labourer***
*Enlisted - August 1915 - joined 7th Battalion The Duke of Cornwall's Light Infantry*
*Died of sepsis 23rd June 1918 (prisoner of war camp) in Berlin - 25 years old*
*He rests in Berlin South-Western Cemetery, Brandenburg.*

**Albert Henry Rowe - *Labourer***
*Enlisted - November 1918 - joined 4th Battalion The Duke of Cornwall's Light Infantry*
*Died of Spanish Flu November 1918 - 18 years old*
*He rests in Watering Hill Cemetery, St Austell.*

**Leonard Warne - *Gardener***
*Enlisted - December 1914 - joined The Royal Engineers*
*Wounded 1918. Died of wounds 21st April 1920, Military Hospital in Davenport - 27 years old*
*He rests in St Bartholomew's Churchyard, Lostwithiel.*

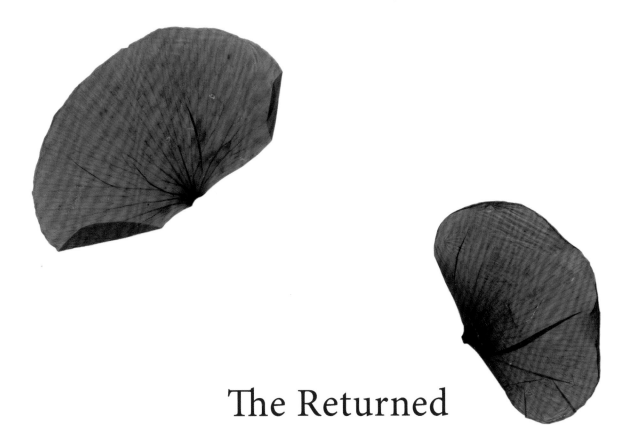

# The Returned

*And remembering also the four outdoor staff of Heligan who returned*

**Fred Paynter - *Stonemason***
*Enlisted - March 1915 - served with The Royal Army Medical Corps*
*& The Royal Engineers & The Tank Corps*
*Returned home unharmed 1919.*

**Archibald Smaldon - *Carpenter***
*Enlisted - May 1916 - served with The Machine Gun Corps*
*& The Army Service Corps & The Royal Engineers*
*Returned home unharmed 1919/20.*

**William 'Keeper' Turner - *Gamekeeper***
*Enlisted - August 1914 - joined The Queen's Own 4th Hussars*
*Served the full length of the war unharmed*
*and returned to Heligan.*

**John Varey - *Gardener***
*Enlisted - October 1916 - served with The Hertfordshire Regiment*
*& The Essex Regiment & The Royal Engineers*
*Returned home injured 28th June 1918, released from hospital February 1919.*

"Will and I used to go to chapel together
and I'd hold his hand and look up at him in his uniform
and think what a fine fellow he was.
But that last time we shared a hymnbook as usual,
I could barely read it because Will's hand was shaking so much.
I didn't understand why at the time."

This touching story, which was shared by Philip,
the youngest brother of William Guy,
was the inspiration for *A Song for Will*.

Will

*These blooms and seeds were collected from
Dud Corner Cemetery, Loos-en-Gohelle, France,
where the name of Corporal William Robins Guy
is etched in stone on the Loos Memorial to the Missing,
along with 20,000 officers and men.*

The Lost Gardens of Heligan

Today, you can visit The Lost Gardens of Heligan, near Mevagissey in Cornwall, at any time of year. There are immaculate Kitchen and Flower Gardens, Pleasure Grounds packed with ancient and exotic plants, beehives and heritage livestock in the pastures. There are lakes and woodland teaming with wildlife, too.

This was also the world of Fred Paynter and William Guy, outdoor staff employed by Squire Jack Tremayne over a hundred years ago, before the outbreak of the First World War. You would never guess now the tragedies that occurred after they enlisted – nor that the gardens later became so neglected and overgrown that even the wild birds departed. I saw their signatures the day they were discovered, back in 1990. To restore the gardens to their past glory involved tracking down old photos and documents and meeting the descendants of those who used to live and work here.

Squire Jack Tremayne's great-great nephew and niece own Heligan today. Squire Jack was a captain in The Duke of Cornwall's Light Infantry (the regiment that Will joined), but he was too old to serve on the battlefront. So Squire Jack's role was managing enlistments – helping to recruit new men to the regiment. He offered Heligan House for use as a convalescent hospital for wounded officers, for indeed, 'war knows no rank'. His mother, Mrs Tremayne (who created the Sun-Dial Garden, which became famous in 1896), was to lose two of her five grandsons.

Mr Griffin was Head Gardener at Heligan in 1914 – and his 'office' still has a fire in the hearth through every winter. The old wage books record him often working in the glasshouses full of exotic fruits and he was in charge of 22 men. These wage books also record the day Fred Paynter enlisted and reveal that, by 1917, so many had departed from Heligan that Fred's father and brother then represented a quarter of the whole outdoor staff. We are so grateful to the local families who have shared memories and mementos of the brave service of their relatives.

Fred                    Squire Jack

Fred, Will, Squire Jack and his mother, Mrs Tremayne, were real people at Heligan in 1914, as was Ida the cook and Mr Griffin, the head gardener. Diggory Abbott was a gardener at Heligan a few years before war broke out, until he moved to work elsewhere. The rest of the characters in this story are fictional – except for Diggory's scarecrow, who remains to this day!

*Candy Smit, Heligan Archivist*

*www.heligan.com*
*For information about our Living Memorial to 'The Gardeners of Heligan House',*
*visit: www.ukniwm.org.uk/63622 and to search for more information on: Guy 240555 and Paynter 57179*
*visit: https://livesofthefirstworldwar.org*

*Also from the award-winning partnership of*
## Hilary Robinson & Martin Impey

ISBN 978-0-9571245-8-5

ISBN 978-0-9571245-7-8

ISBN 978-0-9571245-6-1

ISBN 978-0-9571245-5-4

*'Like us'* on Facebook - Where The Poppies Now Grow

**STRAUSS HOUSE**
PRODUCTIONS

For more information on other titles from Strauss House Productions
www.strausshouseproductions.com

| NAME. | AMOUNT |
|---|---|

A. Snalldon

R. Paynter

J. James

R. Paynter

F. Paynter

J. Holman